At the park

CONTENTS

Welcome to the park......................................2

Morning..4

Midday...8

Afternoon 10

Evening..14

Index..16

Welcome to the park

Most towns have a park.

This park is in a big town.
Lots of people like to visit it.

Morning

Every morning the park keeper opens the gate.
It's still early.

The first people come into the park.
Some of them bring their dog.
They walk the dog every morning.

People go through the park. They are going to work.
They hurry because they don't want to be late.

gardener

rockery

KEEP OFF
THE
GRASS

sign

Children go through the park. They are going to school.
They don't hurry because they want to stay all day!

Midday

There is a lake in the park.

People have picnics by the lake.

They throw bread to the ducks.

There is a café in the park.

Lots of people go there for lunch.

Afternoon

horse chestnut

A class of children are visiting the park.
They are drawing the trees and bushes.

Someone finds a butterfly.
Someone else draws a caterpillar.

WELCOME
TO THIS PLAYGROUND
FOR UNDER 14s ONLY

NO DOGS
NO BALL GAMES
SAY NO TO STRANGE

PLEASE PUT YOUR LIT
IN THE BIN

sign

There is a playground in the park.
Some children go there after school.

They slide on the slide.
They swing on the swings.
Some children play tag.

13

Evening

The last people leave the park. It's late.
Every night the park keeper locks the gates.

It's very quiet. The park is empty now....

.... *or is it?*

Index

bin 4, 15

café 9

gardener 6

horse chestnut 10

lake 8

main gate 4

map 4

park keeper 4, 14

rockery 6

sign 6, 12

The Little Work Plane

Story by Annette Smith
Illustrations by Marina McAllan

Jed was a pilot at a big airport.
He flew the work planes.
They were kept in the big sheds
by the runway.

One day, Jed got a call
from a man at the airport.
"Please come now in your little plane.
We need you to help us."

Jed started up
the engine.

6

The little plane went slowly
down the runway
and stopped by the big planes.

The big planes looked down
at the little work plane and laughed.
"You will have to get
out of our way," they said.
"We are going to take off soon."

A man came running
over to the little plane.
He gave Jed two big bags.

"Take these bags up to the farm
on the big hill," said the man.
"There is so much snow up there
that the farmer can't get out.
He needs this food for his family."

Jed pulled the bags of food
into the little plane,
and it moved slowly
down the runway.

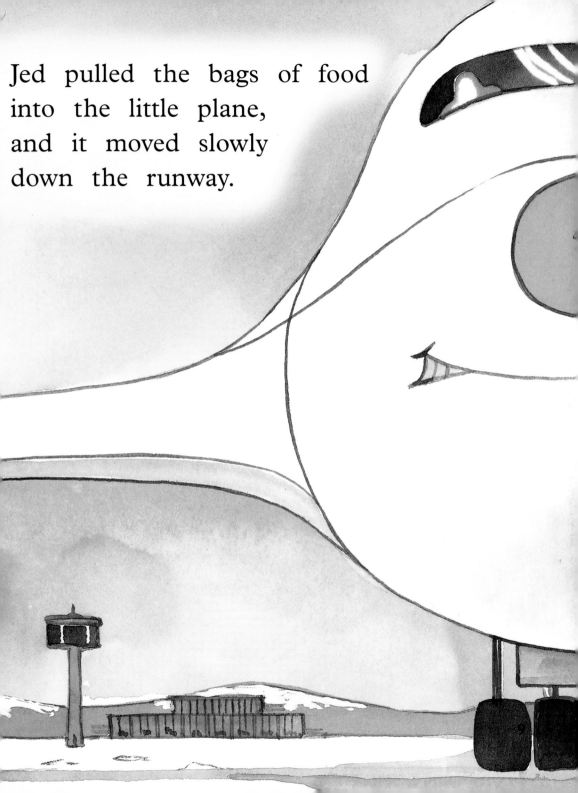

The little plane went faster and faster.
Then away it went up into the sky.

It went out over all the houses
and the farms.

Soon it came to the big hills.
There was snow all over them.

"I hope I can find the farm,"
said Jed.

The little plane flew
around the hills again and again.
Jed looked for the farmhouse.
Then he saw it.

The farmer was outside.
He was waving to the little plane.

"That looks like the place,"
shouted Jed.

Jed pushed the bags of food out.
They fell down
into the snow by the farmer.

"Good work!" shouted the farmer.

And the little plane
flew back to the airport.

The little plane went slowly
past the big planes.

"I did a very good job today,"
said the little plane.
"I **helped** someone who needed me."